Usborne
Memory Games Pad

Phil Clarke

Illustrated by the Pope Twins

Designed by Michael Hill

Edited by Sam Taplin

Memory tips

The puzzles and games in this book will test your memory and help you to improve it. The tips below will make them easier. Your memory works best when you relax and have fun, so remember to do that!

Chunk it

Memorizing a long string of numbers or letters is tricky, but break it up into smaller chunks like a phone number and it's suddenly easier:

483274956 ⟶ 483 274 956

Acrostics

In an acrostic, you use the first letters of a word or phrase to memorize something. For example, to spell "because":

Big Elephants Can Always
Understand Small Elephants.

Rhyme and rhythm

Rhyme, rhythm, or putting something to a tune you know, can really help:

*In fourteen-hundred and ninety-two,
Columbus sailed the ocean blue.*

Picture it

Visual aids really stick in the memory. For example, to remind you how *their* and *there* differ:

the*i*r the*r*e

Crazy connections

Making links to things that are meaningful to you helps you to recall them – the crazier the better. For example, if you met a girl named Sophie Wood, to remember her name you could picture her growing leaves like a tree.

Tell a story

Try turning a list into a story. For example: *milk, eggs, bread, sugar, soap.* A milk carton is stomping on some eggs, the eggs run away and hide behind a loaf of bread. Sugar starts raining down, covering the loaf. The loaf uses some soap to wash it off.

School bags

Look at these bags for one minute, then turn the page and see if you can label them correctly. Turn back to see if you got them right.

Dead battery

Your phone battery is about to die. You have one minute to memorize the numbers of your friends Rebecca and Sol. Then turn the page and try to jot them down.

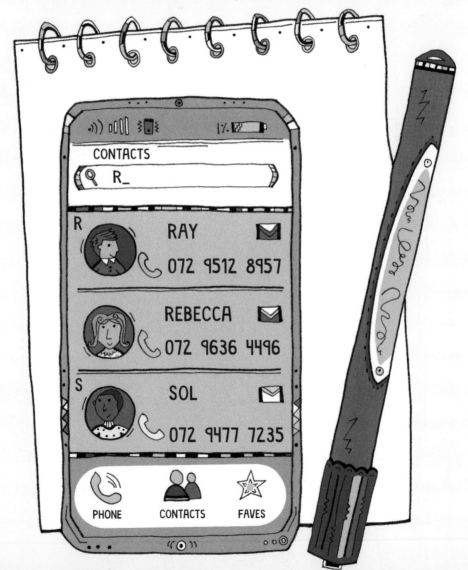

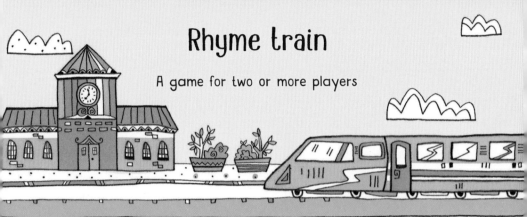

Rhyme train

A game for two or more players

1

One person starts by saying something...

> I went for a run

2

The next player adds another line that rhymes with it.

> I went for a run
> In the sizzling sun

3

The next player repeats what went before, and adds a new line that *doesn't* rhyme.

> I went for a run
> In the sizzling sun – But
> I tripped on a stone

4

The next player adds another line that rhymes with that, and so on, with each pair of lines rhyming.

> I went for a run
> In the sizzling sun – But
> I tripped on a stone – And
> I fell with a moan

5

If anyone gets something wrong, they are out.

> ... But I tripped on a rock
> – I mean a stone!

Party planning

A game for three or more players

1

Someone starts the game by saying something she might bring to a party.

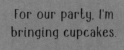

For our party, I'm bringing cupcakes.

2

The next player says what the last person said, then adds his own part:

For our party, Amy's bringing cupcakes and I'm bringing balloons.

3

The next person adds something else...

For our party, Amy's bringing cupcakes, Ben's bringing balloons, and I'm bringing party hats.

4

...and the game continues like this until someone makes a mistake or forgets something. They are out.

5

The last player still in the game wins.

Aquarium

Look at these fish carefully for one minute, then turn the page. See if you can find them among the other fish and circle them, then turn back to see how you did.

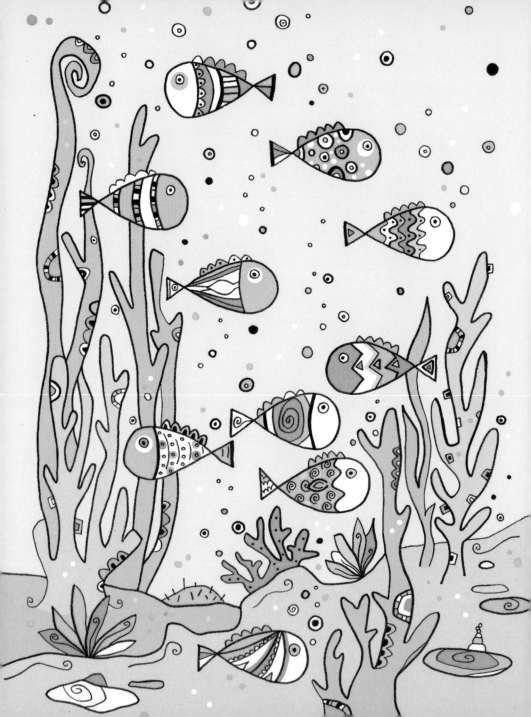

Bird spotting

Read these bird descriptions for one minute, then turn the page. See if you can label all the birds. Turn back to check.

Monday

Male blackbird

Yellow eye-rings

Plain black

Long tail

Tuesday

Female blackbird

Dark brown

Some pale streaks

Wednesday

Short tail

Very pointed beak

Starling

White speckles

Black-brown with a purple-green sheen

Solar system

Look at this picture for one minute to memorize the planets of our solar system in order of their distance from the Sun. Then turn the page and try to number each planet.

 8. Neptune

7. Uranus

6. Saturn

4. Mars

5. Jupiter

3. Earth

1. Mercury

2. Venus

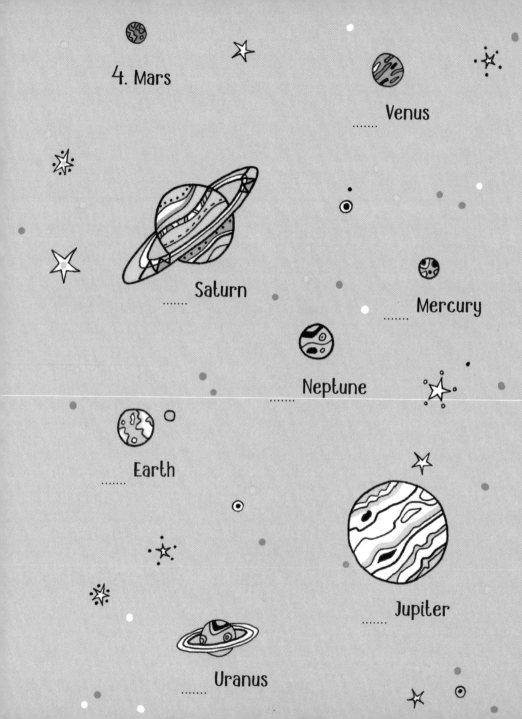

4. Mars

Venus ....

Saturn ....

Mercury ....

Neptune ....

Earth ....

Jupiter ....

Uranus ....

Story time

A game for three or more players

 1

One person makes up
the first part of a story.

 2

The next player repeats it,
then adds another line.

> One day a dog named Max
> was chasing a cat when it
> ran into a haunted house...

> One day a dog named
> Max was chasing a cat when
> it ran into a haunted house.
> Max chased it inside, then
> a ghost appeared...

3

Each player repeats the story
so far and adds a new part.

> One day a dog
> named Max was chasing
> a cat when it ran into a
> haunted house. Max chased it
> inside, then a ghost appeared.
> The ghost said "Don't be scared,
> you can play with my ghost
> dog, Charlie!"

4

If anyone misses anything,
they're out. See how far you can all
get. Can you finish a story together?

Gibberish

A game for three or more players

(1)

In this game you have to remember
lots of nonsense words.

(2)

Sit in a circle. The first player
makes up a nonsense word.

(3)

The next player repeats the
word, and adds their own.

> Snarf

> Snarf wibble

(4)

The players continue like this, adding
more and more nonsense words.

> Snarf wibble
> plink

> Snarf wibble
> plink batang

> Snarf wibble plink
> batang foojah

(5)

Anyone who misses a word, or
says it wrong, is out. How
long can you keep it up?

> Snarf wibble plink
> batang foojah kikitiki
> shlurm zaboogie...
> err, binkidink?

> No, it was binkidonk!

Balloons

Look at the designs on these balloons carefully for one minute, then turn the page and try to draw in all the missing designs. Turn back to see how you did.

Where's Melvyn?

Melvyn the monster has drawn a picture of himself. Look at him closely for one minute then turn the page and see if you can find him among the other monsters.

Time for treats

Look at these cupcakes for one minute, then turn the page and see if you can circle below the two that have been eaten.

Robot recall

Compare these robots for one minute, then turn the page and see if you can mark each statement as true or false. Turn back to find out how you did.

T / F 1. The yellow robot is taller than the blue robot.

T / F 2. The blue robot has bigger hands than the yellow robot

T / F 3. The yellow robot has bigger ears than the blue robot.

T / F 4. The yellow and blue robot have the same kind of feet.

T / F 5. The blue robot has more dials than the yellow robot.

T / F 6. The yellow robot has two eyes.

T / F 7. The blue robot is holding a cog.

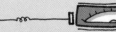

Magic cups

A game for two or more players

1

For this game you'll need three cups, such as paper or plastic cups, and a small ball or other object.

2

One person turns the cups upside-down on a table, and puts the ball under one of them.

3

Then, while the other person watches, they switch the cups around several times.

4

The other person now tries to remember where the ball is.

5

Take turns hiding the ball and guessing.

When I sailed the seven seas

A game for two or more players

1

One person starts by saying something amazing that has two words beginning with **a**:

> When I sailed the seven seas, many wonders did I see: an ant with antlers.

2

The next player repeats what the first person said, then adds a wonder whose words begin with **b**:

> When I sailed the seven seas, many wonders did I see: an ant with antlers and a blue banana.

3

The game continues like this, with each player repeating what went before, and adding new wonders in alphabetical order.

> When I sailed the seven seas, many wonders did I see: an ant with antlers, a blue banana and a chocolate chicken.

4

If anyone forgets a wonder, or mixes up the order, they are out.

> ...a chocolate chicken, a dancing dinosaur, an enormous egg, a giggling goose - no, a flying fish!

Pole position

Look at the cars for one minute, then turn the page and see if you can write the correct number on each one.

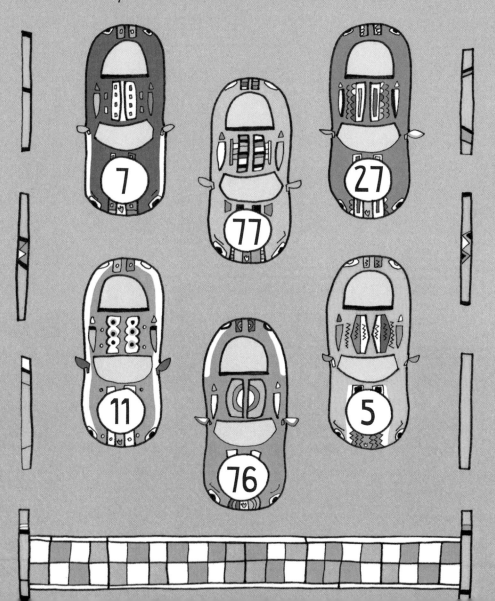

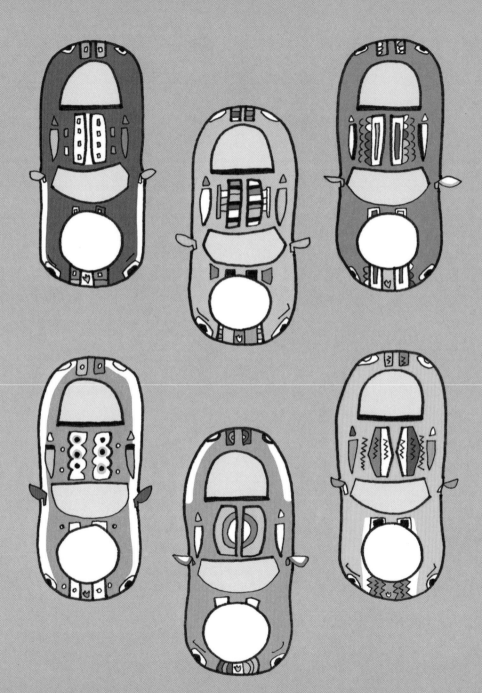

Snowy scene

Look at this snowman for one minute, and try to memorize its details. Now turn the page and try to draw them from memory. Turn back to see how you did.

Draw in the details you recall. How many buttons does the snowman have? How many stripes on its hat? How many stones make up its mouth? How many lines on the carrot?

Picture postcard

Look at this postcard for one minute, then turn the page. Can you circle three differences? Turn back to see how you did.

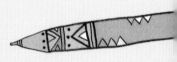

Stolen jewel

The priceless Roscoff Ruby has been stolen from its cabinet. Study the crime scene below for one minute, then turn the page to answer the police's questions. Turn back to see how you did.

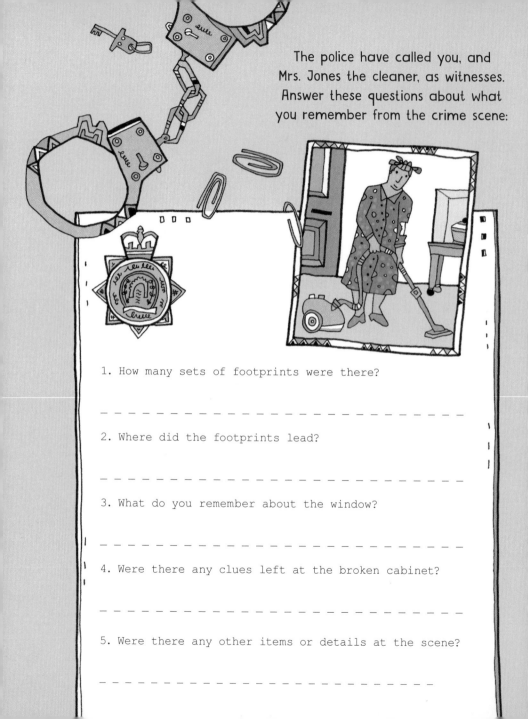

The police have called you, and Mrs. Jones the cleaner, as witnesses. Answer these questions about what you remember from the crime scene:

1. How many sets of footprints were there?

_ _

2. Where did the footprints lead?

_ _

3. What do you remember about the window?

_ _

4. Were there any clues left at the broken cabinet?

_ _

5. Were there any other items or details at the scene?

_ _

Kim's game

A game for three or more players

For this game, you will need a tray, a cloth to cover it, pens and paper, and lots of little objects.

One player gathers 10-15 objects and arranges them on the tray, covered by the cloth.

The cloth is then removed for one minute, and the other players try to memorize the objects.

When the objects are covered again, the players all write down as many as they can remember.

5

Whoever correctly lists the most wins.

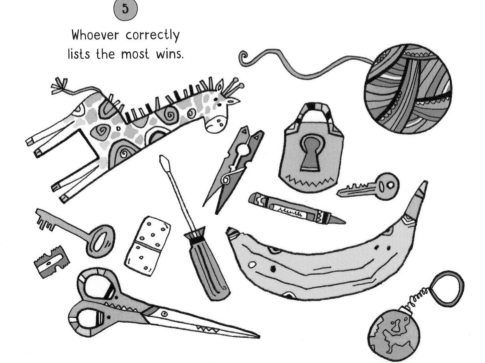

As easy as ZYX

Do you think you'd be able to recite the alphabet backwards? It's not as hard as you might think.

1

Remembering a series of letters (or numbers) is easier if you split it into small groups:

ZYXWVUTSRQP...

ZYX, WV, UTS, RQP...

2

Reading out loud, using rhythm and rhyme will also help it to stick in your memory.

ZYX, WV,
UTS, RQP

3

As you read out the letters, emphasize the rhyming ones at the end of each group:

The last line has a quicker rhythm →

ZYX, WV,

UTS, RQP,

ONM, LKJ,

IHG, FED, CBA!

4

Rehearse until you know it off by heart, then challenge your friends to see if they can learn it too.

Flags

Look closely at these flags for one minute, then turn the page and see if you can correctly label each flag with its country.

Chile

France

Russia

Somalia

Netherlands

Micronesia

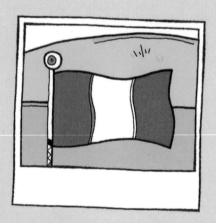

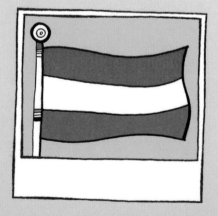

Gingerbread folk

Look at the list of ingredients for one minute, then turn the page and circle as many of them as you can remember. Turn back to see if you got them all.

· Ingredients ·

Brown sugar
Maple syrup
Ginger
Butter
Flour
Salt

Desert island

Carefully study the scene below for one minute, then turn the page and try to draw around the four differences. Turn back to see how you did.

Cast photos

The school show this year is Cinderella. Look at the cast photos below for one minute, then turn the page and draw lines from the children's names to the photos. Turn back to see how you did.

Bella Ball is
Cinderella

Sophie Smith is
the Stepmother

Justin Beaver is
Prince Charming

Bryan O'Leary
is Ermintrude

Wanda Shea is the
Fairy Godmother

Ryan O'Leary
is Griselda

Leroy Jones
is the King

Olivia Green
is the Queen

Cinderella

The Stepmother

Prince Charming

Ermintrude

The Fairy
Godmother

Griselda

The King

The Queen

Leroy Jones   Bryan O'Leary   Justin Beaver   Bella Ball

Olivia Green   Wanda Shea   Ryan O'Leary   Sophie Smith

In my backpack

A game for two or more players

1

Someone begins by saying something he has in his backpack. It can be as silly as you like.

In my backpack I have a woolly hat

2

The next player repeats this, then adds her own part:

In my backpack I have a woolly hat and some maracas.

3

The next person adds something else:

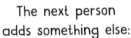
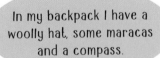

In my backpack I have a woolly hat, some maracas and a compass.

4

The game continues like this until someone forgets something or makes a mistake. They are out.

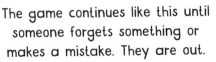

5

The last person still playing wins.

Concentration

A game for four or more players

Everyone sits or kneels in a circle, and chooses a number each.

(2)

You all chant to a rhythm of two thigh slaps followed by two hand claps (see right)

Are you rea-dy?
• • • •

Slap! Slap! Clap! Clap!

If so, let's go!
• • • •

Slap! Slap! Clap! Clap!

(3)

Player 1 continues the rhythm, chanting his own number twice followed by another player's number twice.

1-1-3-3
• • • •

Slap! Slap! Clap! Clap!

3-3-2-2...
• • • •

Slap! Slap! Clap! Clap!

The player whose number was called does the same, and so the game continues.

Anyone who goes wrong is out, but stays in the circle slapping and clapping, so the others must be careful not to call their numbers. Speed up as you go on. The game ends when just two players are left.

Dogs at play

Study the dogs and their toys for one minute, then turn the page and see if you can draw lines to match them up. Turn back to see how you did.

Family tree

Study Sunita's family details carefully, then turn the page and try to answer the questions about how her family are related to each other.

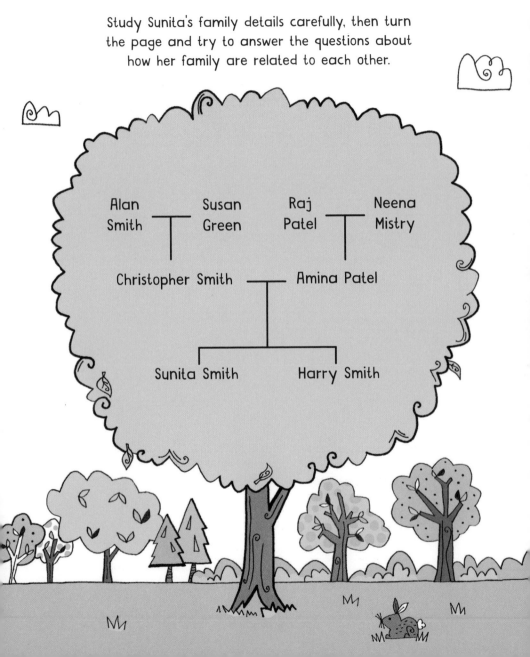

Alan Smith — Susan Green

Raj Patel — Neena Mistry

Christopher Smith — Amina Patel

Sunita Smith   Harry Smith

For each question, circle the correct answer.

1. Sunita's brother is

    a. Barry   b. Harry   c. Raj

2. Sunita's grandfather on her mother's side is

    a. Alan   b. Raj   c. Christopher

3. What relation is Alan to Christopher Smith?

    a. father   b. brother   c. son

4. Which relative is not one of Sunita's grandmothers?

    a. Neena   b. Amina   c. Susan

Game show

Look at the items on the conveyor belt for one minute, then turn the page and see how many you can list. Turn back to see how you did.

CONVEYOR COUNT

Map challenge

Study this map of Southeast Asia for two minutes, then turn the page and see if you can label the countries correctly in the key.

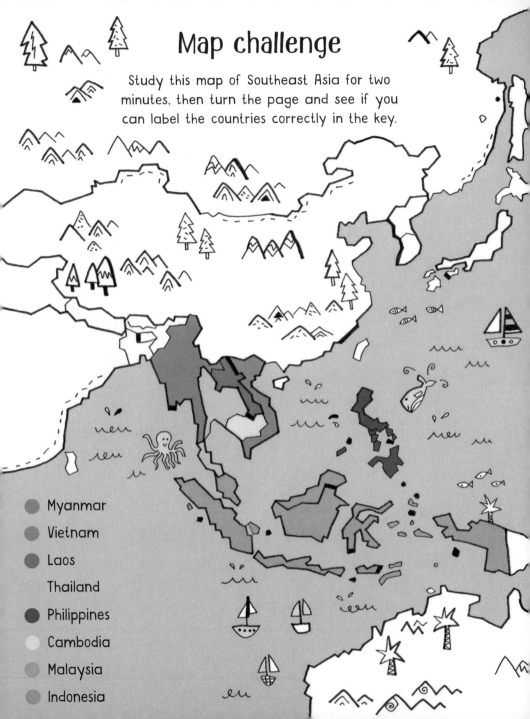

- Myanmar
- Vietnam
- Laos
- Thailand
- Philippines
- Cambodia
- Malaysia
- Indonesia

Memory match game

Cut out the squares below along the dotted lines. Turn them picture-side down on a flat surface, mix them up and spread them out. Take turns turning up two squares at a time. If they match, you win them. If they don't, you turn them back over. Whoever gets the most pairs wins.

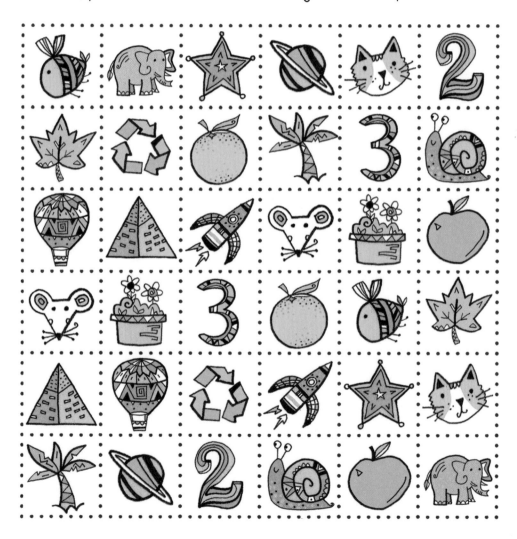

Sports tops

Look at the numbers on these sports tops for one minute, then turn the page and see if you can fill in the blanks. Turn back to see how you did.

Walrus sketch

Study this walrus for one minute, trying to memorize its details. Then turn the page and see if you can draw them from memory. Turn back to see how you did.

What details do you recall? How many whiskers does
the walrus have? How many twirly lines on its side?
Can you remember the patterns on its tusks?

Robot code

Study the key below for two minutes, to learn the code. Then turn the page and see if you can decipher what the robots are saying. Turn back to see how you did.

1 = B
2 = D
3 = E
4 = H
5 = I
6 = L

7 = O
8 = R
9 = S
10 = T
11 = U
12 = W

1 =   5 =   9 = S

2 =   6 = L   10 =

3 = E   7 =   11 =

4 =   8 =   12 =

12-5-6-6   12-3   8-7-1-7-10-9

?

8-11-6-3   10-4-3   12-7-8-6-2

8-3-1-3-6   1-11-10-6-3-8-9

?

!

9-9-4-4   7-8   12-3 - 6-6

,

1-7-10-4   1-3   8-3-12-5-8-3-2

!

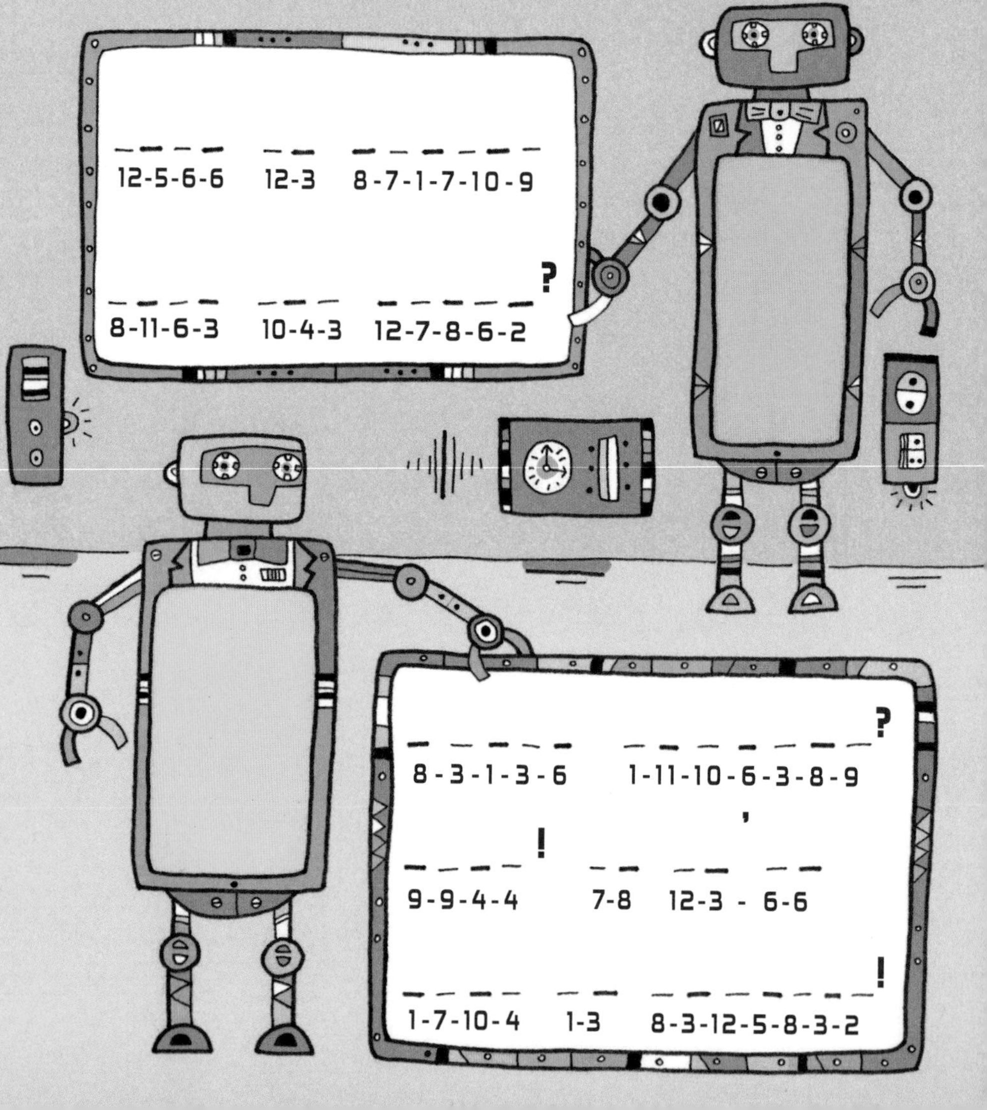

Boating lake

Look at the paddle boats on the lake for one minute, then turn the page and see if you can fill in the missing numbers.

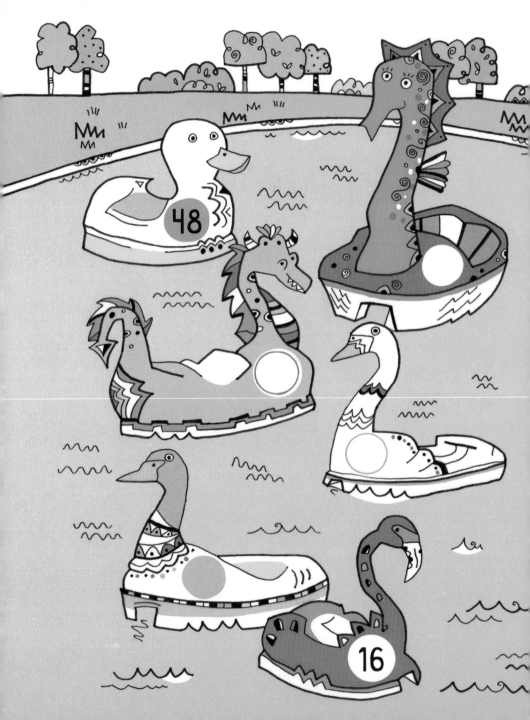

Spelling tricks

You can use memory aids to help you spell tricky words.
There are some examples and challenges below.

1

Take the letters of words you find tricky and turn
them into memorable sentences. For example:

broccoli

Boiled, raw, or carefully
cooked, Oliver loves* it.

(*or loathes it!)

beautiful

Big ears aren't ugly,
they're in fashion:
utterly lovely!

rhythm

Rhythm helps your
two hips move.

separate

Six eager puppies all
run after tiny elephants.

2

Now try making up catchy
phrases to help spell these words:

beginning

....

....

calendar

....

....

definitely

....

....

necessary

....

....

The coin game

A game for two or more players

1

For this game you will need a big pile of mixed coins or board game counters, a cloth or piece of paper to cover them, and something to time yourselves.

2

One player takes five coins and lines them up in any order. You all look at them for five seconds, then cover them up.

3

Start the timer, then everyone races to make the same sequence out of the remaining coins. Whoever completes the sequence correctly in the shortest time wins.

4

When you are all experts at this game, make it more challenging by playing the rule that all the heads and tails must be correct, too.

Countries and capitals

Try to memorize these countries and capitals for one minute, then turn the page and see if you can draw lines to match them up. Turn back to see how you did.

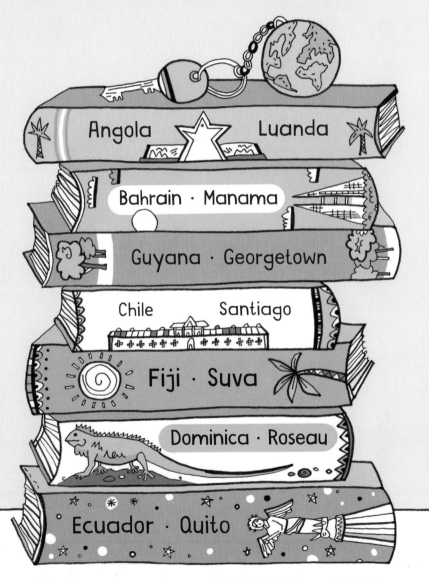

Angola · Luanda

Bahrain · Manama

Guyana · Georgetown

Chile · Santiago

Fiji · Suva

Dominica · Roseau

Ecuador · Quito

Angola	Georgetown
Bahrain	Luanda
Chile	Manama
Dominica	Quito
Ecuador	Roseau
Fiji	Santiago
Guyana	Suva

Route recall

You have to deliver a birthday card to a family friend, but need to follow your parents' directions to find her house. Memorize the directions for one minute, then turn over and see if you can draw your route on the map. Turn back to see how you did.

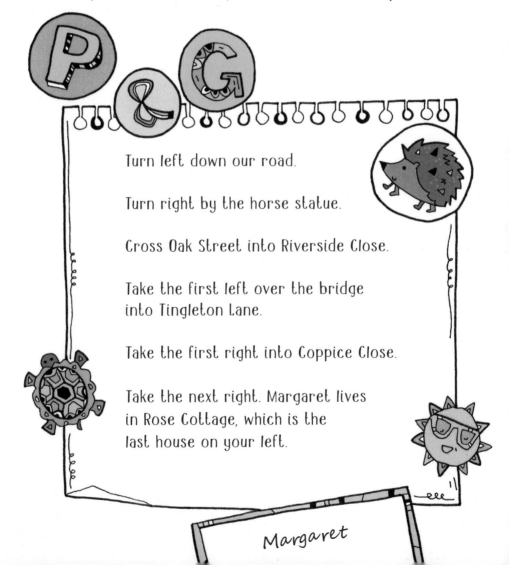

Turn left down our road.

Turn right by the horse statue.

Cross Oak Street into Riverside Close.

Take the first left over the bridge into Tingleton Lane.

Take the first right into Coppice Close.

Take the next right. Margaret lives in Rose Cottage, which is the last house on your left.

Margaret

Interesting insects

Study these four insects for one minute, then turn the page and see if you can circle them among all the other insects. Turn back to see how you did.

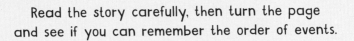

The knight's tale

Read the story carefully, then turn the page
and see if you can remember the order of events.

A KNIGHT was riding through a dark forest
when he heard the sound of crying nearby.

Spurring his horse onwards, he found himself in a ring of
bright red toadstools. To his astonishment, on one of the
toadstools sat a little elf, weeping with his head in his hands.

The knight took pity and climbed down from his mount.
"What is it, small sir, that brings you such sorrow?" he asked.
"Alas!" cried the elf. "The fairy queen has invited me to tea,
and I, a poor wretch, have no gift for her."

The knight smiled sadly. "I have journeyed far and wide," he said,
"and once my saddle-bags held many treasures. But I am sworn to
aid the poor and needy, and there now remain but a few silver coins.
Could these be a gift worthy of her kindness?"

"Oh, sir knight," the elf replied, "you are a credit to your race, but alas!
To our queen treasures of silver and gold are but common trinkets."
But then his bright eye fixed on a locket around the knight's neck.

"Small sir," said the knight with a sigh, "of all my treasures this is
the dearest, for it holds a lock of my true love's hair. But... your need
is greater, so ask and it is yours."

At this the elf vanished. In his place stood a tall, elegant lady in
a long green gown, wearing a crown of leaves and flowers.
"I am the fairy queen," she said, "and you are a knight of true and
noble heart. You may keep your locket, and know this, that your
saddle-bags will always be full of gold. May you long continue in
your kindness to all you meet." And so it was that the knight was
rewarded by the fairy queen.

Number the events from the story in order from 1-8:

The elf was sad because he had no gift.

The knight offered the elf his locket.

The knight heard the sound of crying.

The fairy queen rewarded the knight for his generosity.

The elf vanished.

The knight met a little elf on a toadstool.

The knight was riding through the forest.

The knight offered the elf his silver coins.

What's changed?

An indoor game for three or more players

1

This game is best played in a room all the players know well. Give everyone a minute to look around the room, seeing where everything is.

2

One player (or more, if you want to play in teams) goes out of the room. The others then change something in the room. It must be something clearly visible.

Ideas

· Move a chair · Turn a light on or off · Remove a rug
· Change the time on a clock · Add an item from elsewhere
· Turn something upside down · Open curtains, or a window
· Switch cushions around · Hide a plant or ornament

The players return and try to guess what has changed. Take turns, and see which player or team is best at spotting the changes.

US Presidents

Here's a way to help you memorize lists of names such as historical figures or sports heroes.

1

For example, take the first ten US presidents. Find words that sound like their names, then join them up into a silly story.

1.	George Washington	... George washing
2.	John Adams	... a dam
3.	Thomas Jefferson	... Jeff's
4.	James Madison	... mad son
5.	James Monroe	... Moon rowing
6.	John Quincy Adams	... Quincy
7.	Andrew Jackson	... and Jack
8.	Martin Van Buren	... burning van
9.	William Henry Harrison	... wheelie horizon
10.	John Tyler	... tiles

George was **washing a dam** when he saw **Jeff's mad son** on the **Moon rowing** a boat with **Quincy and Jack**. Suddenly, a **burning van** did a **wheelie** on the **horizon**, spilling a load of **tiles**.

2

Find the words that work best for you. The funnier the story, the more memorable it will be. Try it out on the next ten:

11. James K. Polk
12. Zachary Taylor
13. Millard Fillmore
14. Franklin Pierce
15. James Buchanan
16. Abraham Lincoln
17. Andrew Johnson
18. Ulysses S. Grant
19. Rutherford B. Hayes
20. James A. Garfield

Stars down under

Study these Australian Aboriginal star patterns for one minute, then turn the page and see if you can redraw the lines to complete the constellations.

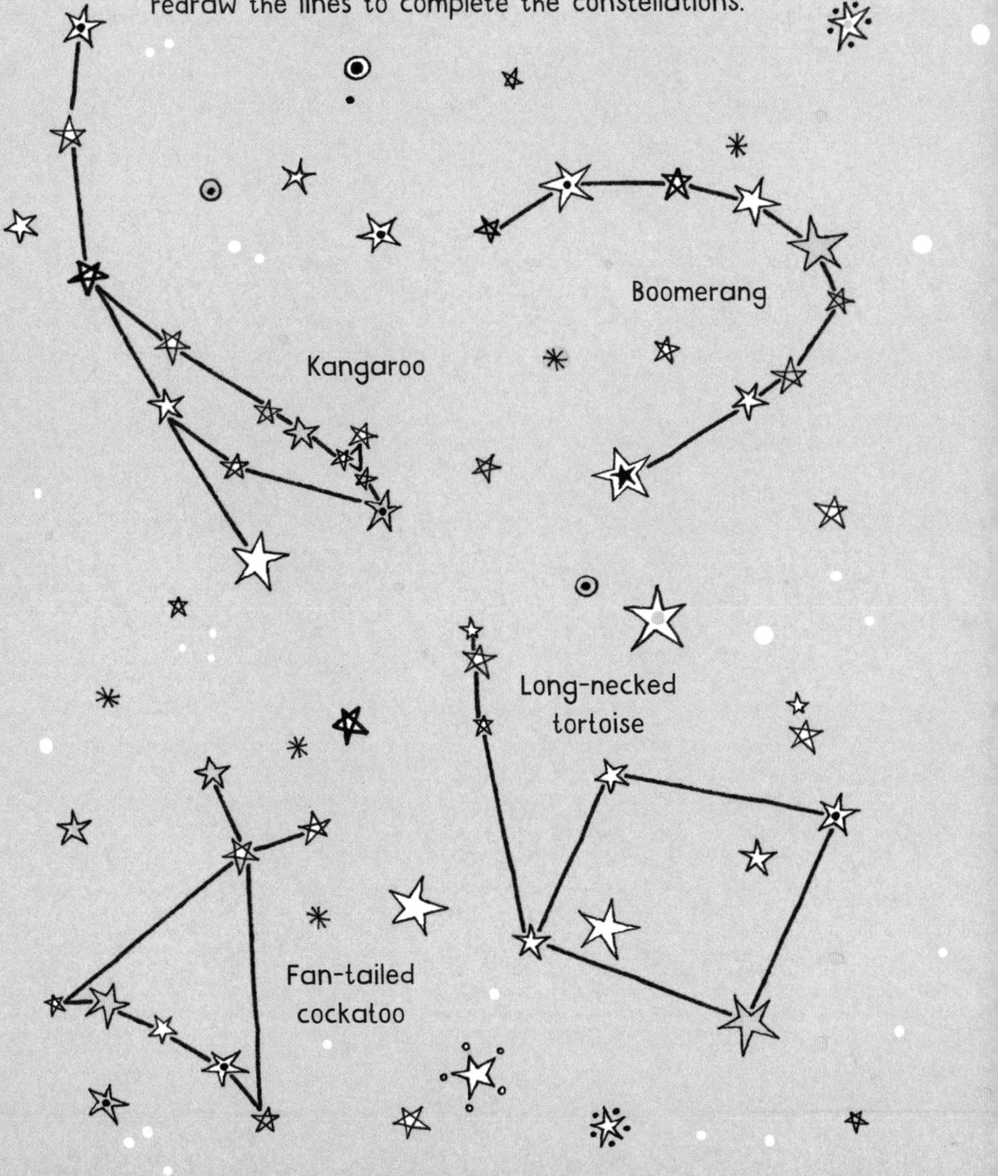

Kangaroo

Boomerang

Long-necked tortoise

Fan-tailed cockatoo

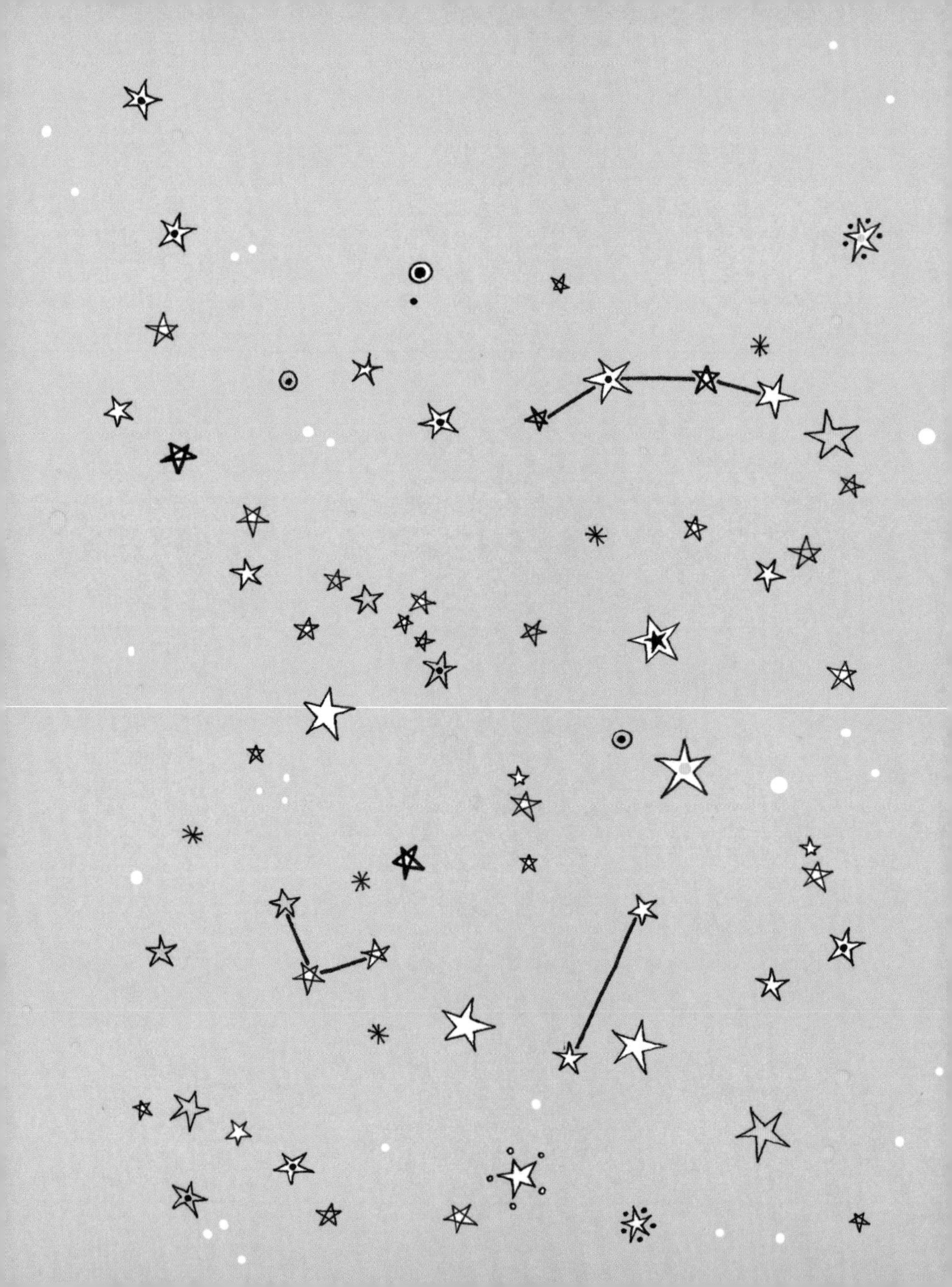

Unicorn meadow

Look at these unicorns for one minute,
then turn the page and see if you
can circle the new unicorn.

Bat sketch

Look at the bat with open wings for one minute, trying to memorize its details. Then turn the page and see if you can draw them from memory.

What details do you recall? Can you draw the bat's face correctly? How many lines are there on its wings? Can you remember the patterns on its body?

Popular pies

Of the 100 pies sold today, which sold best? Read the sales information below carefully, then turn the page and try to circle the pie chart that matches the results best.

SWEETIE'S PIES

15 Blueberry pies

5 Pumpkin pies

20 Cherry pies

25 Pecan pies

5 Banana pies

30 Apple pies

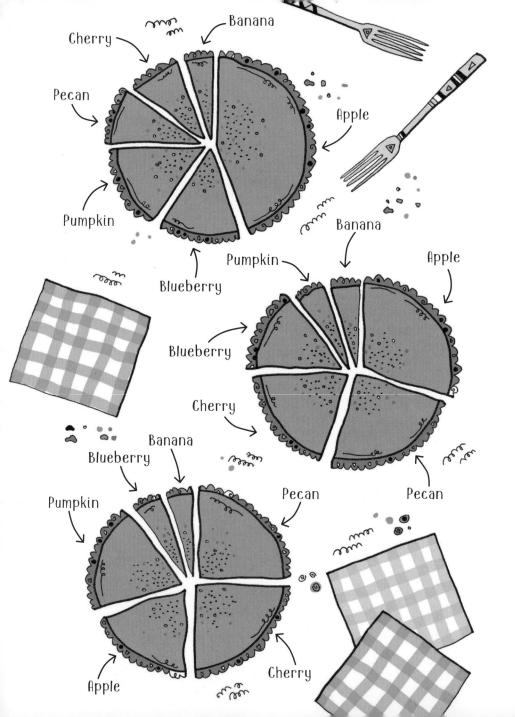

In the museum

Look at the scene below for one minute, then turn the page and see if you can circle four differences. Turn back to see how you did.

Word by word

A game for three or more players

In this game, you tell a story
together, one word at a time.

2

The first player starts by
saying the first word.

Once

3

The second player repeats the
first word, then adds the next.

Once upon

4

The third player continues
in the same way, adding
another word to the sentence.

Once upon a

5

Anyone who forgets
something is out. See
how long you can all
keep the story going.

Once upon
a time

Missing symbols

Mysterious symbols like these have been found on prehistoric pottery. Study them for one minute, then turn the page and see if you can draw in the two missing symbols.

Bug-eyed monsters

Look at these monsters for one minute, then turn the page and see if you can draw the right number of eyes on each one.

Calendar challenge

Try to memorize the picture for each month on
the calendar, then turn the page and see if you can
quickly doodle each one. Turn back to see how you did.

January

February

March

April

May

June

July

August

September

October

November

December

Molehill maze

For this challenge, you'll need something to time yourself.
First, time yourself guiding the mole up out of the molehill.
Then turn the page and see how long it takes you to finish
the maze the second time. How much quicker were you?

Glimpse and go

A game for four or more players

For this game, everyone will need
a piece of paper and a pen.

The first player secretly draws
a fairly complicated picture. Or
this could be done beforehand.

The next player is then allowed to
look at the picture for ten seconds.

This player then redraws the picture
as well as he can from memory.

The following player now
looks at the second player's
picture, and redraws that.

The game continues, with
each player redrawing
the last player's picture.

7

When everyone has played,
the first and last players hold up
their pictures. How did you all do?

Group juggle

A game for five or more players

 1

For this game you'll need three or more small balls, such as tennis balls, juggling balls or softballs.

 2

Everyone stands in a circle. One player starts by calling out someone's name and throwing her the ball.

 3

That player does the same, calling and passing to a player that hasn't caught yet.

 4

The game continues like this until the ball reaches the first player again.

 5

Repeat the same sequence for a couple of rounds. If the ball is dropped, or someone throws wrong, you start again.

 6

Now the first player starts again, and after a throw or two he adds a second ball, and that gets passed around, too.

 7

If you manage to keep it up with two balls, the first player adds a third, and so on. See how many balls you can play with without getting mixed up!

Pattern gallery

Study these patterns for one minute, then turn the page and see if you can shade in all the missing parts. Turn back to see how you did.

X-agonal

Crowd scene

Star field

Blocked in

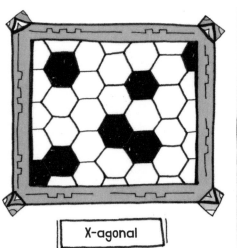

X-agonal

Crowd scene

Star field

Blocked in

Lost cat

Ruby has lost her pet cat, Mr. Tibbles. Study his picture and description carefully, then turn the page and see if you can circle him among all the cats at the Rescue Shelter.

MISSING

Mr. Tibbles

His nose is pink.

The left side of his face is white.

His tail has a white tip.

Spotting butterflies

Look at the butterfly guide for one minute, studying the patterns on the open and closed wings of each species. Then turn the page and draw two arrows from each name label to show which is which.

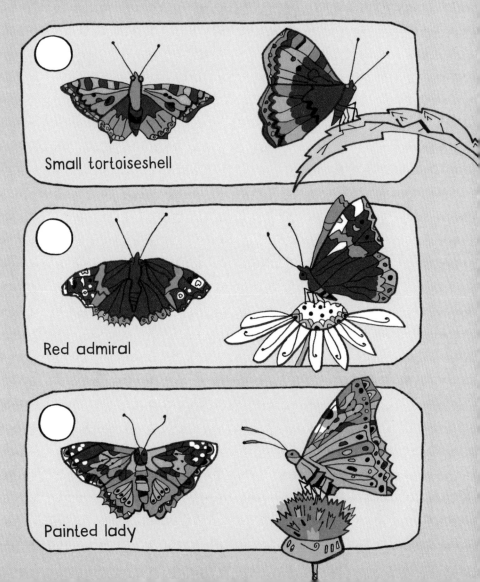

Small tortoiseshell

Red admiral

Painted lady

Red admiral (2)

Small tortoiseshell (2)

Painted lady (2)

Christmas wishes

Look at these longed-for Christmas gifts for one minute, then turn the page and try to label the wrapped presents correctly. Turn back to check.

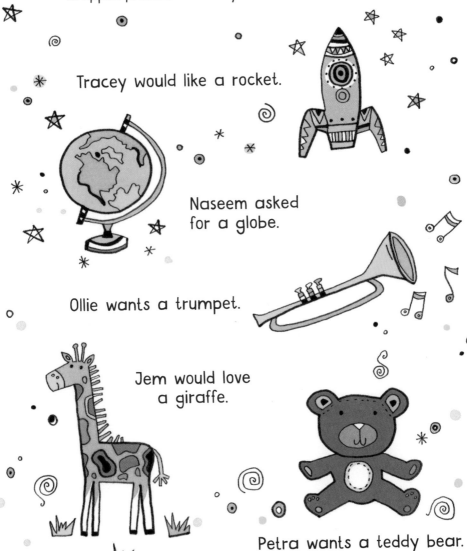

Tracey would like a rocket.

Naseem asked for a globe.

Ollie wants a trumpet.

Jem would love a giraffe.

Petra wants a teddy bear.

Balloon festival

Look at this scene for one minute,
then turn the page and try to
circle the four differences.

JUNE'S BALLOONS

Where are the bears?

Look at all the teddy bears for one minute, then turn the page and circle the two that have changed places.